Please return / renew by da̲̲ ̲̲.̲̲.̲̲.̲̲.̲̲wn.
You can renew it at:
norlink.norfolk.gov.uk
or by telephone: 0344 800 8006
Please have your library card & PIN ready

NORFOLK LIBRARY
AND INFORMATION SERVICE

Let's Mix!

Written by Shari Last

LONDON, NEW YORK, MUNICH,
MELBOURNE and DELHI

Editor Shari Last
Designer Rhys Thomas
Pre-Production Producer Marc Staples
Producer Louise Minihane
Managing Editor Elizabeth Dowsett
Design Manager Ron Stobbart
Publishing Manager Julie Ferris
Art Director Lisa Lanzarini
Publishing Director Simon Beecroft

Designed for DK by
Thelma-Jane Robb

Reading Consultant
Maureen Fernandes

First published in in Great Britain in 2014 by
Dorling Kindersley Limited
80 Strand, London, WC2R 0RL
A Penguin Random House Company

10 9 8 7 6 5 4 3 2 1
001—255729—Sep/2014

Colour reproduction by Alta Image, UK
Printed and bound in China by South China

Discover more at

www.dk.com
www.LEGO.com

Contents

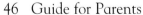

Hello Mixels™!

Mixels love to sing,
dance, jump and twirl.
Most of all, they
love to MIX!

Mixels have the most fun when they mix up all their pieces with their friends and combine into something new. Let's mix!

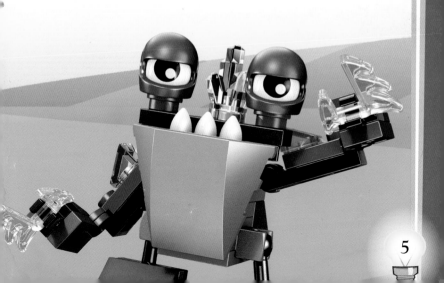

The Frosticons

When Flurr, Slumbo
and Lunk mix, they
become colder than ice itself!

They turn into this big
Frosticons Max! His hands
can freeze fire, and his breath
can turn lava into snow.

Make Ice Lollies with the Frosticons!

The Frosticons love cold things like ice towers, snow, a chilly breeze and, of course, ice lollies! Learn how to make ice lollies the Frosticon way.

1   Choose your favourite flavour.

Flurr

I love cookironis, but Slumbo prefers coconapples. What do you like?

2 Mix your food together until it tastes perfect. Then take a little nap.

Lunk

3 Tickle Lunk's nose to make him sneeze on your mixture. Hey presto! It has turned to delicious ice.

ACH-OOO!

Slumbo

Making ice lollies is hard work!

The Infernites

Hello Flain. Hello Vulk.
Hello Zorch. These Infernites
are hot, fiery and happy.

When they mix together,
they become this huge Infernites
Max! He has scorching hair and
a red-hot sense of humour.

Time to Mix

Help! Zaptor and Zorch
need to cross the river.
Time to mix!

Now they have Zaptor's energy
and Zorch's fire-power to lift off.
They can fly over the river!

The Spikels

Scorpi, Footi and Hoogi look
scary, but they love to hug.
They also love to mix.

This big Spikels Max still looks
scary, but he is very gentle.
Just watch out for his spikes!

It is my Birthday!

You are invited to my party!

When: Tomorrow afternoon

Where: My house!

RSVP: Scorpi

Pillow fights

Fantastic games

Yummy food

An amazing cake

I can't wait to see you!
Love, Scorpi

The Cragsters

The Cragsters are
strong, but slow.
When they need
speed, Krader,
Seismo and Shuff
mix together!

This big Cragsters Max has
hands that can smash rocks.
His feet are super fast.
No obstacle can slow him down!

24th Annual TUNNEL DIGGING RACE

KRADER
also known as
"The Rock Smasher"

VS

VS **SHUFF**
also known as
"Wrecking Ball"

SEISMO
also known as
"Feet of Fear"

FIND OUT WHO CAN DIG THE LONGEST TUNNEL!

TOMORROW
in the Great Cavern,
at 10 a.m.

The Glorp Corp

Glomp, Glurt and Torts are
ready for the ultimate swamp
adventure. Let's mix!

This gooey Glorp Corp Max
leaps over muddy puddles
and swims through swamps.
Goo shoots from his fangs!
The next adventure
will be a slimy one!

23

The Wiztastics

Wizwuz, Mesmo and Magnifo
love doing magic tricks.
Their magic show is
the greatest in the land.

When they mix, they become this
flying Wiztastics Max. He can
do any magic trick you want.

Silly or Quiet?

Glomp and Mesmo
are very different.
Glomp loves
playing silly games.

Mesmo is a
lot quieter.

When Glomp and Mesmo mix,
they make up a game to play
together. It is silly AND quiet.
Perfect!

The Fang Gang

Oh dear.
Chomly
is hungrier
than ever!

Jawg and Gobba
want to help. MIX!

This hungry Fang Gang Max can find the best food around. His huge teeth chomp through anything. Dinner time!

Gobba's Diary

Yesterday, my amazing tongue saved the day.
As usual, I was planting things to eat
on our farm, together with my
best friends Chomly and Jawg.

We planted many new things: a table,
an apple, three pots, some cat hair
and a soggy stick. We sat and waited
for everything to grow into delicious food.

Just as we were about to cook the soggy
stick, my tongue told me that something
was wrong. I asked my friends to wait.

Just then,

the Wiztastics

came running onto

My tongue knows all sorts of things about food.

our farm, looking

for Magnifo's magic wand.

When they saw the soggy stick,

they were excited... it was Magnifo's wand!

Magnifo and his friends were so pleased

to get it back. Luckily, we still had lots

of other food to eat.

Hooray for my tongue!

The Electroids

How many Electroids
does it take to change
a lightbulb? Three!
Teslo, Zaptor and
Volectro.

When they mix, they become a
crazy, crackling Electroids Max.
Now they are tall enough
to reach the lightbulb.

33

A Lesson in Lightning
by: Zaptor

Electroids get their energy from lightning!
In school, we learnt all about lightning fields,
where Electroids catch lightning.

Lightning
strikes here

The energy
goes down
the pole,
where it is
stored for
later.

35

The Flexers

Who is this bug-like Mixel?

He is what you get when
Tentro, Kraw and Balk mix.

This big, cheerful Flexers Max
loves climbing walls and
bouncing from place to place.

37

All Mixed Up!

Mixing is so much fun that the Mixels do it all the time! Here are some amazing mixed up Mixels.

Fiery **Flain** and energetic **Teslo** are super-charged and ready for adventure!

Sleepy **Slumbo** and forgetful **Balk** can't remember when they last cut their moustache.

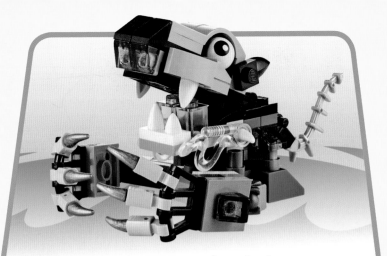

Glurt and **Hoogi** both love seeing their friends. Now they can give them a huge spiky hug!

Gooey **Torts** and happy **Wizwuz** are going to think up a slimy magic trick.

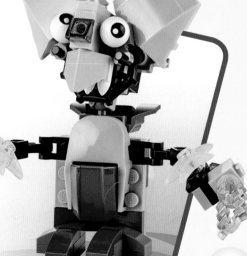

All the Mixels

Here are all nine types of Mixel.
Which is your favourite?

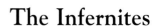

The Frosticons

The Infernites

The Spikels

The Cragsters

The Glorp Corp

The Wiztastics

The Fang Gang

The Electroids

The Flexers

Quiz

1. What colour are the Frosticons?

2. Which Mixels are fiery?

3. Which Mixel invited you to his birthday party?

4. Which Mixels are good at digging tunnels?

5. Which Mixels are ready for a swamp adventure?

6. Which Mixels love doing magic tricks?

7. What kind of Mixel is Chomly?

8. Who has an
amazing tongue?

9. What kind of Mixels are
Teslo, Zaptor and Volectro?

10. How many
Mixels are there?

Answers on
page 45

Glossary

cavern
a large cave

coconapple
a fruit that is
half a coconut,
half an apple

combine
mix together

cookironi
a snack that is
half a cookie,
half macaroni

fiery
something made
of fire or flames

lava
hot, melted rock

magician
someone who
performs magic

obstacle
something that
gets in your way

scorching
extremely hot

ultimate
the best

wrecking ball
a big, heavy
ball that
destroys things

Index

Answers to the quiz on pages 42 and 43:
1. Blue 2. The Infernites 3. Scorpi 4. The Cragsters
5. The Glorp Corp 6. The Wiztastics
7. A Fang Gang Mixel 8. Gobba 9. Electroids
10. Twenty seven

Guide for Parents

DK Reads is a three-level reading series for children, developing the habit of reading widely for both pleasure and information. These books have exciting running text interspersed with a range of reading genres to suit your child's reading ability, as required by the school curriculum. Each book is designed to develop your child's reading skills, fluency, grammar awareness and comprehension in order to build confidence and engagement when reading.

Ready for a *Beginning to Read* book

YOUR CHILD SHOULD

- be using phonics, including combinations of consonants, such as bl, gl and sm, to read unfamiliar words; and common word endings, such as plurals, ing, ed and ly.

- be using the storyline, illustrations and the grammar of a sentence to check and correct their own reading.

- be pausing briefly at commas, and for longer at full stops; and altering his/her expression to respond to question, exclamation and speech marks.

A Valuable And Shared Reading Experience

For many children, reading requires much effort but adult participation can make this both fun and easier. So here are a few tips on how to use this book with your child.

TIP 1: Check out the contents together before your child begins:

- Read the text about the book on the back cover.
- Read through and discuss the contents page together to heighten your child's interest and expectation.
- Briefly discuss any unfamiliar or difficult words on the contents page.

- Chat about the non-fiction reading features used in the book, such as headings, captions, recipes, lists or charts.

This introduction helps to put your child in control and makes the reading challenge less daunting.

TIP 2: Support your child as he/she reads the story pages:

- Give the book to your child to read and turn the pages.

- Where necessary, encourage your child to break a word into syllables, sound out each one and then flow the syllables together. Ask him/her to reread the sentence to check the meaning.

- When there's a question mark or an exclamation mark, encourage your child to vary his/her voice as he/she reads the sentence. Demonstrate how to do this if it is helpful.

TIP 3: Praise, share and chat:

- The factual pages tend to be more difficult than the story pages, and are designed to be shared with your child.

- Ask questions about the text and the meaning of the words used. Ask your child to suggest his/her own quiz questions. These help to develop comprehension skills and awareness of the language used.

A FEW ADDITIONAL TIPS

- Try and read together every day. Little and often is best. After 10 minutes, only keep going if your child wants to read on.

- Always encourage your child to have a go at reading difficult words by themselves. Praise any self-corrections, for example, "I like the way you sounded out that word and then changed the way you said it, to make sense".

- Read other books of different types to your child just for enjoyment and information.

Here are some other DK Reads you might enjoy.

Beginning to Read

LEGO® Legends of Chima™: Tribes of Chima
Enter the mysterious land of Chima and discover
the amazing animal tribes who live there.

LEGO® Friends: Perfect Pets
Learn all about Mia, Olivia, Andrea, Stephanie and
Emma's pets – and discover how much fun pets can be!

Star Wars Rebels™: Meet the Rebels
Meet the *Star Wars Rebels* heroes and learn all about the
enemies from the evil Empire they are rebelling against.

Starting to Read Alone

LEGO® Legends of Chima™: Heroes' Quest
Who are the mysterious Legend Beasts? Join the heroes
of Chima on their quest to find these mythical creatures.

LEGO® Friends: Summer Adventures
Enjoy a summer of fun in Heartlake City with Emma,
Mia, Andrea, Stephanie, Olivia and friends.

Star Wars™: What Makes a Monster?
Meet some of the most fearsome monsters in the *Star Wars* galaxy.
Discover brutal beasts, scary hunters and strange creatures.